pig

cow

horse

water

fox

D0433601

Five steps for enjoyable reading

Follow the steps below to help your child to become a confident and independent reader:

Step 1
Read the story aloud to your child. Run your finger under the words as you read.

One sunny day, the little old woman looks in her cook book. "I'll bake a gingerbread man," she decides. So she mixes and rolls and cuts out the gingerbread man. Then she pops him in the oven.

8

Step 2
Look at the pictures and talk about what is happening.

Step 3

Read the simple text together.
Help your child to sound out the
letters of the bold words: **o-l-d.**

The **old** woman makes
a gingerbread man.

9

Step 4

When your child is
ready, encourage them
to read the simple lines
on their own.

Step 5

Help your child to complete the puzzles
at the back of the book. You'll also find
more notes on helping your child to read.

THIS BOOK BELONGS TO

....

Retold by Katherine Sully
Illustrated by Gail Yerrill

Reading consultant: Geraldine Taylor

Marks and Spencer plc
PO Box 3339
Chester CH99 9QS

shop online
www.marksandspencer.com

Copyright © Exclusive Editions Publishing Ltd 2012

First Readers is a trade mark of Exclusive Editions Publishing Ltd

All rights reserved. No part of this publication may be reproduced,
stored in a retrieval system or transmitted by any means,
electronic, mechanical, photocopying, recording or otherwise
without the prior permission of the copyright holder.

ISBN 978-1-84461-583-4
Printed in China

THE GINGERBREAD MAN

M&S

One sunny day, the little old woman looks in her cook book.

"I'll bake a gingerbread man," she decides. So she mixes and rolls and cuts out the gingerbread man. Then she pops him in the oven.

The **old** woman makes
a gingerbread man.

But, oh dear! When the little old woman opens the oven door, she has a big surprise. The gingerbread man jumps up and runs out through the door.

"Come back!" she calls.

"You are not going to eat me!" says the gingerbread man."

The gingerbread **man**
runs off. "Come back!"

The little old
woman and the little
old man chase after
the gingerbread man.

"Run, run, as fast as
you can. You can't catch
me, I'm the gingerbread
man!" he laughs.

"A **pig** can't eat me,"
he says.

The little old woman,
the little old man and
the pig chase after the
gingerbread man.

"A **cow** can't eat me,"
he says.

"Run, run, as fast as you can. You can't catch me, I'm the gingerbread man!" he laughs.

The little old woman, the little old man, the pig and the cow all chase after the gingerbread man.

He runs past the horse.

"You are **big**, but I am fast," he says.

17

"Run, run, as fast as you can. You can't catch me, I'm the gingerbread man!" he laughs. The little old woman, the little old man, the pig, the cow and the horse all chase after the gingerbread man.

They all **run** after him.

Soon, the gingerbread man
comes to a river.
"Oh no, how will I get
across?" he cries.

"I will help you," says
the **fox**.

"Hold onto my tail," says the
fox. So the gingerbread man holds
onto the fox's tail. The fox jumps
into the water.

"I will get **wet**," says the gingerbread man.

"Jump onto my back," says the fox. So the gingerbread man jumps onto the fox's back.

The gingerbread man sees the little old woman, the little old man, the pig, the cow and the horse far behind him.

"**Now** they can't eat me,"
he says.

"You are getting heavy," says the fox. "Jump onto my nose." So the gingerbread man jumps onto the fox's nose.

But it is a trick! As soon as they are safely on the other side of the river, the fox tosses the gingerbread man into the air... and gobbles him up!

And that is the **end** of the gingerbread man.

Puzzle time!

Which two words rhyme?

man big fox run pig

Which word does not match
the picture?

tail

nose

oven

Which word matches the picture?

how

cow

now

Who bakes the gingerbread man?

little old woman

little old man

horse

Which sentence is right?

You can't catch me.

You can catch me.

Puzzle time answers

Which two words rhyme? man (big) fox run (pig)
Which word does not match the picture? tail nose (oven)
Which word matches the picture? how (cow) now
Who bakes the gingerbread man? little old woman little old man horse
Which sentence is right? You can't catch me. You can catch me.

Great ways to help reading

Traditional tales and fairy stories are a great way to begin reading practice. The stories and characters are familiar and lively. Here are some of the ways you can help your child read the words they may come across for the first time.

Letters and sounds

Your child probably already knows their ABC. But teaching small letter-sounds (phonemes) is an excellent way to help children to read and spell. Phonics teaches that the sounds of letters and combinations of letters make words. Help your child to sound out the bold phonic words on the right-hand page:

r-u-n = run   p-i-g = pig

When your child is confident, try some words that have sounds that blend together. They will come across the same blends in new words. Encourage your child to sound out new words that blend different letter sounds:

f-a-<u>st</u> = fast   b-a-<u>ck</u> = back

Sight words

Some words come up again and again. These high-frequency words will quickly become recognized by sight. The simple children's sentences in this book are made up of these important, frequently used words:

the   and   little